Peter Pauper's Book of Fun

WITH ILLUSTRATIONS BY
ALBERT EISLER

THE PETER PAUPER PRESS
MOUNT VERNON · NEW YORK

Peter
Pauper's
Book of
Fun

Puzzles and Problems

Fish Tale

A fish's head is as long as its tail. The head, tail, and body are fifteen inches long. If the head were twice as long as it is, the head and tail together would be as long as the body. How long is each?

Body, nine inches; head, three inches; and tail, three inches.

This Is Easy!

How would you write the number one hundred with six nines?

$99 \frac{99}{99}$

Frog in the Well

A frog at the bottom of a forty-foot well, every day jumps up three feet and at night falls back two. How many days will it take him to get out of the well?

Thirty-eight days. He jumps all the way out the last day.

Sheep and Turkeys

A drove of sheep and turkeys have 99 heads and feet. How many are there of each, if there are twice as many turkeys as sheep?

Nine sheep and eighteen turkeys.

Cats and Rats

If three cats can catch three rats in three minutes, how many cats could catch one hundred rats in one hundred minutes?

The same three cats.

How Many Cows?

A boy, driving some cows, was asked how many cows he had. He said, "When they are in line there are two cows ahead of a cow, two cows behind a cow, and one cow in the middle." How many cows had he?

Three.

Hens and Eggs

If a hen and a half lays an egg and a half in a day and a half, how many eggs will six hens lay in six days?

Twenty-four. At this ratio, a hen will lay two-thirds of an egg a day. Six hens would lay four eggs a day and twenty-four in six days.

Strange Animal

What animal is it which walks first on four legs, later on two, and in old age on three?

The human. As a baby, he crawls; then walks on two legs; and when old, uses a cane.

Digit Problem

Arrange the digits 1, 2, 3, 4, 5, 6, 7, 8, 9, 0, so that they will equal 100.

50½ and 49 38/76.

THE SAD STORY OF THE FOX, THE GOOSE AND THE CORN

A farmer on his way to market with a fox, a goose, and a basket of corn, comes to a river. The boat will carry only the farmer and one of his charges. This presents a problem, for if he takes the corn and leaves the fox and the goose, the fox will eat the goose. If he takes the fox and leaves the goose and the corn, the goose will eat the corn. He must plan so that these com-

8

binations are not left together on the other side of the river as well. How does he do it?

He takes over the goose; returns and takes over the fox. He brings back the goose and leaves the goose while he takes over the corn. He returns for the goose.

A Sheep Story

Say out loud: A man had twenty sick sheep and one died; how many did he have left?

19. (*Twenty sick* sounds like *twenty-six*.)

Boy On the Train

A boy is on a train, which is moving at the rate of sixty miles an hour. He jumps straight up three feet. Where does he land?

In the same place from which he jumped.

The Two Farmers

Farmer A said to Farmer B, "If you will sell me seven acres of your farm, I will have twice as much land as you." But Farmer B said to Farmer A, "If you will sell me seven acres of your farm, I will have just as much land as you." How much land did each have?

A had 49 acres and B had 35 acres.

What Coins?

A man has $1.15 in six coins. He cannot make change for a dollar, a half dollar, a quarter, a dime, or a nickel. What coins did he have?

A half dollar, a quarter, and four dimes.

A Question of Dozens

What is the difference between six dozen dozen and a half dozen dozen?

Six dozen dozen is 6 x 12 x 12 = 864; half a dozen dozen is 6 x 12 = 72.

Bottle and Cork

A bottle and a cork cost $1.10, the bottle costing $1.00 more than the cork. Can you tell what the cost of each was?

The bottle cost $1.05 and the cork cost 5 cents.

Mathematical "If"

If a fourth of forty is six, what is a third of twenty?

Four. If a fourth of forty were six, a half of forty would be twelve and a third of twenty would be four.

The Apples

Two boys are apple salesmen and each sells thirty apples a day. The first boy sells his apples two for a nickel and so receives for them seventy-five cents. The second boy sells his apples three for a nickel and receives for them fifty cents. The total received by both boys for the day's sales would be one dollar and twenty-five cents, as follows:

30 apples at 2 for 5 cents = $0.75
30 apples at 3 for 5 cents =   .50

One day, however, boy number one was sick and the other boy took his apples to sell for him. Instead of selling two apples for a nickel and three apples for another nickel, he put them all together and sold them five for a dime.

60 apples at 5 for 10 cents = $1.20

The problem is to find what became of the other nickel.

After ten sales have been made, all the three-for-a-nickel apples are sold. The boy continues to sell apples which should be sold two for a nickel, at five for a dime.

11

Trick With Figures

Request the individuals in a group to write down a number of three figures. This should be written from numbers that will reverse and subtract; as 942, from which take 249. (If the number 249 is written first, it cannot have 942 taken from it, so ask them to start with a large number and then use smaller numbers.) After they have written a number, and then reversed it and subtracted, you can tell them their answers if they will tell you the left-hand figure.

The middle number will always be nine and the last number will always be nine minus the first number. Example: $942 - 249$ equals 693. You are told the first number, 6. The middle number is always nine. The last number is nine minus the first number, 6.

Farm Deal

A trader buys 100 head of animals and pays $100 for them. He buys cows at $10, hogs at $5, and chickens at 50 cents. How many of each does he buy?

One cow, nine hogs, and ninety chickens.

It Can Be Done!

From 19 take 1 and leave 20.

From XIX take I and leave XX.

Cannibals and Missionaries

Three missionaries and three cannibals come to a river in Africa and desire to cross. The boat will only carry two. All the missionaries can row, but only one of the cannibals, cannibal I. The trips must be arranged so that the cannibals will never outnumber the missionaries. In other words, one missionary must never be left with two cannibals or two missionaries with the three cannibals. They were able to get across, but how was it done?

Cannibal I takes over one cannibal and leaves him. He then takes another cannibal and leaves him. When cannibal I returns with the boat two missionaries go over, one of them remaining while the other returns bringing a cannibal with him. One missionary then goes over with cannibal I. A missionary then returns with a cannibal, but leaves cannibal I on the other side. The two missionaries then cross over and turn over the boat to cannibal I, who makes two other trips over for the cannibals, bringing one at a time.

13

SERIES PROBLEM

Study the numbers of each series listed below, determine what law governs the selection of the numbers and write the next two numbers of each series.

Allow three minutes.

1.	1	3	5	7	9	11	—	—
2.	8	4	7	3	6	2	—	—
3.	9	1	2	8	3	4	—	—
4.	1	7	2	7	3	7	—	—
5.	2	1	1	3	1	1	—	—
6.	8	6	4	2	7	5	—	—
7.	37	30	29	22	21	14	—	—
8.	1	12	3	11	5	10	—	—
9.	1	4	9	16	25	36	—	—
10.	1	4	2	8	4	16	—	—

1.	13	15
2.	5	1
3.	7	5
4.	4	7
5.	4	1
6.	3	1
7.	13	6
8.	7	9
9.	49	64
10.	8	32

14

THE FLYING BEE

Two trains leave two towns fifty miles apart. They run toward each other. One of the trains runs thirty miles an hour and the other twenty. A bee, flying at the rate of fifty miles an hour, leaves as the fast train does and meets the slow train. It turns and comes back and meets the fast train; it turns again and in this way keeps on flying back and forth between the trains until they meet. How far does the bee fly?

Fifty miles. As one runs twenty and the other thirty miles an hour, the trains would meet in one hour. The bee then flies only one hour, hence only fifty miles.

SEND MORE MONEY

Substitute digits for the letters so that this makes a correct addition:

$$
\begin{array}{r}
S\ E\ N\ D \\
M\ O\ R\ E \\
\hline
M\ O\ N\ E\ Y
\end{array}
$$

$$
\begin{array}{r}
9\,567 \\
1\,085 \\
\hline
10\,652
\end{array}
$$

Mrs. Bailey couldn't remember the price of the tube of the excellent new toothpaste she had recently purchased, but she did remember that the toothbrush which she bought at the same time cost just three times as much, and that the sum of the digits of the total of the two items was 14. She had given a dollar bill and received some change, so now you know how much she paid for the toothpaste. You won't even need a pencil to figure it out!

The toothpaste costs seventeen cents, and the brush, fifty-one cents. We know from the problem that the total must be a number divisible by four and that its digits must be 5 and 9, 6 and 8, or 7 and 7. The only number divisible by 4 that can be formed from these couples is 68, hence this must be the amount paid by Mrs. Bailey.

ARRANGING AND ADDING

Arrange the digits from 1 to 7 so that they will add up to 100.

$15 + 36 + 47 + 2 = 100.$

16

Riddle Me These

What ship has no captain but two mates?

Courtship.

What did the big firecracker say to the little firecracker?

"My pop's bigger than your pop."

What time of the day was Adam created?

A little before Eve.

If a chicken could talk, what kind of language would it speak?

Foul language.

What is worse than raining cats and dogs?

Hailing taxis.

When do you have four hands?

When you double your fists.

How can a girl keep a boy's love?

By not returning it.

Who was the most popular actor in the Bible?

Samson. He brought down the house.

What made the lobster blush?

It saw the salad dressing.

There is a girl in a butcher shop in Chicago who is 6 feet 8 inches tall, has a 42-inch waist, and wears number 12 shoes. What do you think she weighs?

She weighs meat.

What is worse than a giraffe with a sore throat?

A centipede with sore feet.

I can run but I can't walk. What am I?

Water.

If your uncle's sister is not your aunt, what relation is she to you?

Your mother.

What did Paul Revere say when he finished his famous ride?

"Whoa!"

What has eighteen legs and catches flies?

A baseball team.

Spell "deterioration" with only two letters.

DK.

What room can no one enter?

A mushroom.

What is the best way to keep fish from smelling?

Cut off their noses.

When the clock strikes thirteen, what time is it?

Time to have the clock fixed.

If a biscuit is a soda cracker, what is an ice pick?

A water cracker.

What falls often but never gets hurt?

Rain.

It occurs once in every minute, twice in every moment, and yet never in one hundred thousand years. What is it?

The letter M.

What are the three easiest ways to spread gossip?

Telegraph, telephone — and tell a girl.

Put 2 and 2 together and make more than 4.

22.

Why isn't your nose twelve inches long?

Because it would be a foot.

Why does the Indian wear feathers in his hair?

To keep his wigwam.

Why is it useless to send a telegram to Washington today?

Because he is dead.

If you throw a blue stone into the Red Sea, what will it become?

Wet.

A man bought two fishes and had three when he got home. How can you explain it?

He had two flounders — and one smelt.

Why is it impossible for a lisper to believe in young ladies?

Because with him every miss is a myth.

What is it that is always coming but never arrives?

Tomorrow. When it arrives, it is today.

Why can hens lay eggs only during the day?

Because after dark they are roosters.

What animal took the most baggage into Noah's ark; and what animals the least?

The elephant took his trunk, but the fox and the rooster took only a brush and a comb between them.

What two vegetables begin and end with two letters in the same order?

Tomato and onion.

What is worse than biting into an apple and finding a worm?

Finding half a worm.

Who was the most successful doctor in the Bible?

Job, because he had the most patience.

What word of three syllables contains twenty-six letters?

Alphabet.

How can you keep a rooster from crowing on Sunday morning?

By killing him on Saturday night.

Why did Fred's mother knit him three socks when he was in the army?

Because Fred wrote he had grown another foot.

Which moves faster, heat or cold?

Heat, because you can catch cold.

When is it socially correct to serve milk in a saucer?

When you're feeding the cat.

How does a Model-T Ford remind you of a schoolroom?

It has a lot of little nuts inside with a crank up front.

How many bushel baskets full of earth can you take out of a hole two feet square and two feet deep?

None. The earth has already been taken out.

When is a student hungriest?

When he devours his books.

When a man marries how many wives does he get?

Sixteen: four richer, four poorer, four better, four worse.

Why are promises like fat ladies who faint in church?

Because the sooner they are carried out the better.

If your nose runs and your feet smell, what is the matter with you?

You are built upside down.

Jokes and Laughter

"Name four animals of the cat family."
"The father cat, the mother cat, and two kittens."

Nurse — "Well, Sonny, you have a new baby brother for a Christmas present."
Sonny — "Oh, great! May I be the first to tell Mother?"

25

Director — "That Indian wants two hundred dollars to act the part."

Producer — "Give him a hundred. We need only a half-breed."

A sincere friend is one who says nasty things to your face, instead of saying them behind your back.

"Mother," said the boy, "will you help me with some words? Is it correct to say you 'water a horse' when he's thirsty?"

"Yes, quite correct."

"Then (picking up a saucer) I'm going to milk the cat."

"My husband certainly does enjoy smoking in his den. Does your husband have a den?"

"No, he growls all over the house."

A conceited actor was boasting: "Why, at every performance, during the last act, I have the audience glued to their seats!"

"Oh, my!" exclaimed his friend. "How clever of you to think of it!"

Hubby — "You call that a hat? My dear, I'll never stop laughing."

Wifey — "Oh, yes you will and I'll tell you when: the bill will arrive tomorrow."

"Why don't you settle the case out of court?" said the judge to the litigants before him.

"Sure, that's just what we were doing, Your Honor, when the police came."

An insurance agent was teaching his wife to drive, when the brakes suddenly failed on a downhill grade.

"I can't stop it," she cried. "What'll I do?"

"Don't panic," said her husband, "just hit something cheap."

Mother — "Who ever taught you to use that dreadful, dreadful word you just said, Danny dear?"

Danny — "Santa Claus, mama."

Mother — "Santa Claus?"

Danny — "Yes, mama, when he fell over a chair in my room the night before Christmas."

Judge — "You stole eggs from this man's store. Have you any explanation?"

Accused — "Yes. Your Honor, I took them by mistake."

Judge — "How is that?"

Accused — "I thought they were fresh."

"I see in the paper that a widower with nine children out in Iowa has married a widow with seven children."

"That wasn't a marriage, that was a merger."

"Lizzy swears that she has never been kissed by a man."

"Well, isn't that enough to make any girl swear?"

A nut shop displays this sign: "If our peanuts were any fresher, they'd be insulting."

Visitor — "Well, Bill, how do you like your baby sister?"

Bill — "Oh, she's all right, but there are lots of things we needed more."

Child — "Mother, may I have a nickel for the old man who is outside crying?"

Mother — "Yes, dear, but what is the old man crying about?"

Child — "He's crying, 'Peanuts, five cents a bag.'"

"You say the water that you get here is unsafe? Tell me, just what precautions do you take against it?"

"First we filter it, then we boil it, then we chlorinate it."

"Yes."

"Then we drink beer."

Teacher — "What is an octopus?"

Pupil — "An eight-sided cat."

A teacher called for sentences using the word "beans."

"My father grows beans," said one farmer's child.

"My mother cooks beans," said another pupil.

Then a third answered: "We are all human beans."

"Mother, I just took a splinter out of my hand with a pin."

"A pin! Don't you know that's dangerous?"

"Oh, no, Mother, I used a safety pin."

Dentist — "Open wider please — wider."

Patient — "A-A-A-Ah."

Dentist (inserting rubber gag, towel and sponge) — "How's your family?"

"None of these dirty little jobs for me," said the college graduate, "I want to do something big and something clean."

"Then wash an elephant."

Freshman — "But I really don't think I deserve a zero."

Prof. — "Neither do I, but it is the lowest grade I'm allowed to give."

"How many times must I tell you, Willie, that you must keep your eyes closed during prayer."

"Yes, mamma, but how do you know I don't?"

Wife — "I've bought you a beautiful surprise for your birthday."

Husband — "Let's see it."

Wife — "Wait a minute till I put it on."

One of the girls was wearing an engagement ring, but no one at the office noticed it. Finally in the afternoon, when some of the other typists were nearby, she stood up suddenly.

"My, it's hot in here," she said. "I think I'll take off my ring."

"Why did you leave your job?"

"Illness. The boss got sick of me."

Pupil — "Do you think it's right to punish people for things they haven't done?"

Teacher — "Why, of course not!"

Pupil — "Well, I haven't done my home work."

Medical Professor — "What would you recommend for a person eating poisonous mushrooms?"

Student — "A change of diet."

"Where's Bill?" asked a neighbor boy one winter afternoon.

"Well," said Bill's brother, "if the ice is as thick as he thinks it is, he's skating. If it's as thin as I think it is, he's swimming."

After her first horseback ride, a young lady was heard to make this comment: "I never imagined anything filled with hay could ride so hard!"

"You should meet my husband. He makes a living with his pen."

"Oh, so he's a writer?"

"No, he raises pigs."

"What is the plural of man, Oscar?" asked the teacher.

"Men," answered Oscar.

"And the plural of child?"

"Twins."

"How did your wife get on with her reducing diet?"

"Great! — she disappeared completely last week!"

The minister looked at Mr. Willoughby sadly and said, "I'm told you went to the ball game Sunday, instead of going to church."

"That's a lie," cried Mr. Willoughby, flushing a deep red, "and I've got the fish to prove it."

Advice to farmers: To keep milk from turning sour you should keep it in the cow.

Mother—"What do you want to take your cod liver oil with, today, Junior?"
Junior — "With a fork."

Teacher — "John, what is a cannibal?"
John —"Don't know, Miss Tweet."
Teacher — "Well, if you ate your father and mother, what would you be?"
John — "An orphan, Miss Tweet."

"Dear Miss Fairfax: How should a lady walk with a gentleman?"
"When a lady and a gentleman are walking on the sidewalk the lady should walk inside the gentleman."

"What makes this meat taste so queer?" asked the young husband.
"I can't imagine," replied his bride, "I burned it a little but I put sunburn oil on it at once."

Wife, showing a new hat to her husband: "It didn't cost a thing, dear. It was marked down from $20 to $10, so I bought it with the $10 I saved!"

"Say, that's a bad wound on your forehead. How did you get it?"

"I bit myself."

"Come, come; how could you bite yourself on the forehead?"

"I stood on a chair."

Mrs. Newlywed — "I'm terribly sorry, dear, but dinner is a little burnt tonight."

Mr. Newlywed — "What? Was there a fire at the delicatessen?"

"Is man an animal?"

"Yes: man is an animal split half way up and walks on the split end."

"What is puppy love?"

"It's the beginning of a dog's life."

"Johnny," said the teacher, "why don't you wash your face? I can see what you had for breakfast this morning."

"What did I have, teacher?"

"Eggs."

"You're wrong, teacher. That was yesterday."

"What do you think of our two candidates for mayor?"

"Well, I'm glad only one can be elected."

A man bought a canary from a pet store. "You're absolutely sure this bird can sing?" he asked.

"He's a wonderful singer."

A week later the customer reappeared. "Say! This bird you sold me is lame!"

"Well, you said you wanted a singer, not a dancer."

Correct this sentence: "It was me who broke the window."

"It wasn't me who broke the window."

"Is the doctor in?" inquired the caller.

"Nope," answered his little boy.

"Do you know when he'll be back?"

"Nope! — he went on an eternity case."

"Define parallel lines."

"Parallel lines never meet unless you bend one or both of them."

Quizzle Me These

How hot is the sun?

The temperature at the flaming surface is estimated at 11,000 degrees Fahrenheit. Inside the sun it is far hotter — perhaps 40,000,000 degrees. At these intense heats atoms break down and convert into other atoms — exactly as in atomic or fission bombs — releasing new vast quantities of heat as they do so.

What is the brightest star we can see from Earth?

Sirius, the Dog Star, in the constellation Canus Major, the Great Dog.

Which species in the animal kingdom has the largest brain in proportion to its size?

The ant.

Can furniture make noise at night?

Yes. Furniture, and houses too, make creaking noises as the wood in them expands or contracts with changes of temperature and moisture. These noises take place by day as well as by night — but since most other noises are hushed then, we hear the wood noises more at night.

What is the origin of the word "dollar" and the dollar sign?

The S in the dollar sign is a corruption of the figure 8, from the Spanish "piece of eight" which had a value of eight smaller coins. The parallel lines represent the Pillar of Hercules, or passageway between the Atlantic and the Mediterranean. "Dollar" derives from "thaler" a coin equivalent to a piece of eight but coming from Joachims*thaler*, a silver-mining town in Bohemia.

If the age of the universe could be said to be one year, how long has Man lived in it?

Fifteen minutes.

Where and when was George Washington inaugurated first president of our country?

On the balcony of the old Federal Building located at Broad and Wall Streets in lower Manhattan in New York City. His inauguration took place April 30, 1789.

What was the name of Lindbergh's plane used on the first non-stop solo flight over the Atlantic? The date?

The Spirit of St. Louis. 1927.

What were the Seven Wonders of the ancient world?

The Pyramids of Egypt, the Hanging Gardens of Babylon, the Statue of Zeus at Olympia, the Temple of Artemis at Ephesus, the Mausoleum at Halicarnassus, the Colossus of Rhodes, the Pharos of Alexandria.

How does a bird fly?

A bird flies by pressing down upon the air with its wings. In this way it lifts itself up.

What bird in this country does a sun dance, and can be seen dancing if one gets up at daybreak to watch?

The domesticated turkey. Both male and female perform curious high-stepping awkward up-and-down jumps, varied by forward spring-like movements and interrupted by strutting and hopping and singing, very early in the morning.

Which gland in the human body is comparable to a thermostat in a household heating system?

The thyroid gland, a small, spongy gland, which straddles the windpipe just below the larynx.

What does the distress signal SOS stand for?

SOS does not stand for anything. It is merely a combination of letters easily transmitted and received by wireless.

Who was Sir Galahad?

In the Legend of King Arthur, Sir Galahad was the noblest knight of King Arthur's Round Table. He was the leader in the search for the Holy Grail — the cup from which Christ was supposed to have drunk during the Last Supper.

How long can a whale stay under water?

Twenty minutes. Although whales live in water, they are mammals, not fish.

Four states remained neutral in the Civil War. Which were they?

Missouri, Kentucky, Maryland and Delaware.

How much would a ton of gold weigh at the earth's center?

Nothing. Gravitational pull would be equal in all directions.

How many ways can you change a dollar, using only the common coins: halves, quarters, dimes, nickels and cents?

There are 293 different ways. See how many you can figure out.

What was the cost of World War II to the taxpayers of the United States?

$349,778,608,870. In round figures, 350 billion dollars.

What is a balanced diet?

A balanced diet is one which includes some of the following every day: 1. Milk, or milk products. 2. Citrus fruits, tomatoes, or raw salad greens. 3. Green or yellow vegetables. 4. Other vegetables or fruits, including potatoes. 5. Bread or cereal. 6. Meat, fish, or poultry. 7. Eggs (three or four a week).

What is the oldest city in America?

St. Augustine, Florida, which was settled September 1565, by Don Pedro Menendez.

When did Washington, D.C., become the capital of the United States?

In 1799, during John Adams' administration.

For what crime was Captain Kidd hanged?

Captain Kidd was hanged for murder. He hit one of his seamen over the head with a bucket and killed him. The charge of piracy was never proved.

What is the common ancestor of all flowers?

The lowly buttercup.

Upon whose death were these words said: "Now he belongs to the ages"?

Upon the death of Abraham Lincoln, by Edwin M. Stanton, Secretary of State.

What did the Greeks call the Goddess Venus?

Aphrodite, and worshiped her as the Goddess of Beauty and Love.

What is our national anthem; who is its author; and when was it written?

The Star-Spangled Banner, written by Francis Scott Key, in 1814.

When was Julius Caesar assassinated?

44 B.C.

Alfred Bernhard Nobel, the Swedish inventor, donated a large fortune to the establishment of a Prize for Peace, as well as other prizes. From what invention did his fortune derive?

From the invention of dynamite.

What are tides?

Tides are the alternate rising and falling of water in oceans and other large bodies of water caused by the gravitational pull of the moon, and to a lesser extent of other planets and stars.

What is Braille?

Braille is a system of raised dots punched into special Braille paper. The dots form symbols which blind persons can feel with their finger tips, and thus read.

Is it true that mosquitoes prefer blondes to brunettes?

Yes, the skin of most blondes is less resistant.

What is a sponge: animal, vegetable or mineral?

The sponge is an animal. What we use as a sponge is really the skeleton of the animal.

Is water hotter before it boils, or after?

Before. As soon as it boils, some heat is released.

Which language is spoken by the greatest number of the earth's inhabitants?

Chinese, spoken by approximately 650 million people.

Which is the highest mountain peak in North America?

Mount McKinley in Alaska. It is 20,300 feet high.

How long does it take the earth to make one complete revolution on its imaginary axis?

Twenty-three hours, 56 minutes and 4.1 seconds.

Is the newly-hatched crocodile larger or smaller than the egg from which it has emerged?

Three times as large.

How large a part of the animal kingdom do insects comprise?

Four-fifths.

What is a snorkel?

A snorkel is a ventilation device for submarines consisting of air intake and exhaust tubes. With a snorkel a submarine can remain submerged for long periods.

What is the dog population of the United States?

Somewhere between twenty-two million and twenty-eight million. In round figures, there are twenty-five million dogs in the United States.

Can goats eat tin cans?

No. They cannot. But goats will lick or chew anything made of minerals.

How many quills has a porcupine?

Approximately thirty thousand.

There is only one kind of tissue in the human body which does not renew itself. What is it?

The enamel of our teeth.

How many words does an average educated man use?

Between three thousand and five thousand.

Where does chocolate come from?

Chocolate is made by grinding the kernels of the seeds of the cacao tree which grows in South America, the West Indies and on the Gold Coast of Africa.

Do boats *without* motors have the right of way over boats *with* outboard motors?

Yes. This is the rule of the waterways.

Can a chipmunk climb a tree?

Yes. A chipmunk has been seen on an upper branch of an oak tree, hanging on for dear life and proceeding with extreme caution as he seizes an acorn and stuffs it into his cheek pouch.

What is a flock of geese called?

A flock of geese is known as a "gaggle" on the ground, and a "skein" when the geese take to the air.

Can you keep a mackerel alive in a dish-panful of salt water?

No. The mackerel will drown because he is forced to swim so slowly that the current produced by the movement of his gills would not provide sufficient oxygen for the fish to live.

What is Brass?

It is an alloy of copper and zinc, harder and stronger than either of the metals from which it is made.

Did August always have thirty-one days?

August originally had thirty days until Augustus Caesar decided it should have thirty-one days. He took one day from February to give the month of August as many days as July, named after his predecessor, Julius Caesar.

Does the weather vane point in the direction of the wind?

No. It points in the opposite direction.

Are the stripes of the zebra white or black?

The stripes are white, and the background black. Zebras are descended from solid colored dark animals, and the white stripes are actually tufts of white hair.

It has been found that the typical American reader reads too slowly for convenience and actual comprehension. About what is the average reading rate?

Two hundred and fifty words a minute.

Looney Limericks
for Rollicking Laughter

There's a girl out in Ann Arbor, Mich.,
To meet whom I never would wich.,
　　She'd gobble ice cream
　　Till with colic she'd scream,
Then order another big dich.

There was a young man of Bengal,
Who went to a fancy-dress ball;
    He went, just for fun,
    Dressed up as a bun,
And a dog ate him up in the hall.

❧

There once was a lady named Harris,
That nothing seemed to embarrass
    Till the bath salts she shook
    In the tub that she took,
Turned out to be plaster of Paris.

❧

A two-toothed old man of Arbroath
Gave vent to a terrible oath.
    When one tooth chanced to ache,
    By an awful mistake
The dentist extracted them both!

❧

An epicure, dining at Crewe,
Found quite a large mouse in his stew.
    Said the waiter, "Don't shout,
    And wave it about,
Or the rest will be wanting one, too!"

There was a young girl named Bianca,
Who slept while the sloop was at anchor;
    But awoke, with dismay,
    When she heard the mate say:
"We must pull up the topsheet and spanker."

               ❧

An oyster from Kalamazoo
Confessed he was feeling quite blue,
    "For," he said, "as a rule,
    When the weather turns cool,
I invariably get in a stew!"

               ❧

There once was a young man named Hall
Who fell in the spring in the fall.
    'Twould have been a sad thing
    Had he died in the spring,
But he didn't — he died in the fall.

               ❧

There was a young lady of Stornaway,
Who by walking, her feet had all worn away.
    Said she, "I won't mind,
    If only I find
That it's taken that terrible corn away."

There was an old party of Lyme,
Who lived with three wives at one time.
 When asked, "Why the third?"
 He replied, "*One's* absurd,
And bigamy, sir, is a crime!"

 ❧

A boy who played tunes on a comb,
Had become such a nuisance at homb,
 His ma spanked him, and then —
 "Will you do it again?"
And he tearfully answered her "Nomb."

 ❧

There once was a man of Calcutta
Who spoke with a terrible stutter.
 At breakfast he said,
 "Give me b-b-bread,
And b-b-b-b-b-b-butter."

 ❧

There once lived a certain Miss Gale,
Who turned most exceedingly pale,
 For a mouse climbed her leg
 (Don't repeat this, I beg),
And a splinter got caught in its tail.

A smiling young lady of Riga,
Once went for a ride on a tiger;
    They returned from the ride
    With the lady inside,
And the smile on the face of the tiger.

A mathematician named Haines
After infinite racking of brains
    Now says he has found
    A new kind of sound
That travels much faster than planes.

A dentist whose surname was Moss,
Fell in love with the charming Miss Ross;
    But he held in abhorrence
    Her Christian name Florence
So he called her his dear Dental Floss.

❦

There was a young lady of Crete,
Who was so exceedingly neat,
    When she got out of bed
    She stood on her head,
To make sure of not soiling her feet.

❦

There was a young lady named Rood,
Who was such an absolute prude
    That she pulled down the blind
    When changing her mind,
Lest a curious eye should intrude.

❦

A menagerie came to our place,
And I *loved* the Gorilla's grimace.
    It surprised me to learn
    That he *owned* the concern
Being human, but odd in the face.

A cannibal bold of Penzance
Ate an uncle and two of his aunts,
    A cow and her calf,
    An ox and a half —
And now he can't button his pants.

❦

There was a young lady of Ealing,
Who thought her friends very unfeeling;
    When she had scarlet fever
    They wouldn't receive her,
So she called on them when she was peeling.

❦

An indolent vicar of Bray
Let his lovely red roses decay;
    His wife, more alert,
    Bought a powerful squirt,
And said to her spouse, "Let us spray."

❦

There was an old spinster from Fife,
Who had never been kissed in her life;
    Along came a cat,
    And she said "I'll kiss that!"
But the cat meowed: "Not on your life!"

There was a young lady named Stella
Fell in love with a bow-legged fella,
    The venturesome chap,
    Let her sit in his lap
And she plummeted down to the cella.

❧

There was a young lady of Flint,
Who had a most horrible squint.
    She could scan the whole sky
    With her left-handed eye,
While the other was reading small print.

❧

There was an old man of Blackheath,
Who sat on his set of false teeth;
    Said he, with a start,
    "O Lord, bless my heart!
I've bitten myself underneath!"

❧

There was a young lady of Kent,
Who always said just what she meant;
    People said, "She's a dear —
    So unique — so sincere —"
But they shunned her by common consent.

There was a young lady named Perkins,
Exceedingly fond of small gherkins.
　　She went out to tea
　　And ate forty-three,
Which pickled her internal workings.

～

There was an old lady of Rye,
Who was baked by mistake in a pie;
　　To the household's disgust
　　She emerged through the crust,
And exclaimed, with a yawn, "Where am I?"

～

I wish that my room had a floor;
I don't care very much for a door,
　　But this walking around
　　Without touching the ground
Is getting to be such a bore.

～

A sensitive girl named O'Neill
Once went up in the big Ferris Wheel;
　　But when half-way around
　　She looked down at the ground,
And it cost her a two-dollar meal.

A thrifty young fellow of Shoreham
Made brown paper trousers and woreham;
    He looked nice and neat
    Till he bent in the street
To pick up a pin: then he toreham.

❧

There was a fair maid from Pomona —
The first time she ate a bologna
    She said: "It is queer,
    And I really do fear
You must help me remove its kimona."

❧

I sat next to the Duchess at tea;
It was just as I feared it would be:
    Her rumblings abdominal
    Were simply phenomenal,
And everyone thought it was me!

❧

An amoeba named Sam, and his brother,
Were having a drink with each other;
    In the midst of their quaffing
    They split their sides laughing
And each of them now is a mother.

There's a notable clan yclept Stein:
There's Gertrude, there's Ep, and there's Ein.
    Gert's prose has no style,
    Ep's statues are vile,
And nobody understands Ein.

❧

There was a young man so benighted,
He never knew when he was slighted.
    He went to a party,
    And ate just as hearty
As if he'd been really invited.

❧

A fly and a flea in a flue
Were imprisoned, so what could they do?
    Said the fly, "Let us flee!"
    "Let us fly!" said the flea.
So they flew through a flaw in the flue.

❧

There was an old man of the Nore,
The same shape behind as before.
    They did not know where
    To offer a chair,
So he had to sit down on the floor.

Silly Problems

Punctuate the sentence: I saw a five dollar bill lying in the street.

[MAKE A DASH FOR IT]

What is the meaning of:

○

M.D.

B.A.

D.D.S.

M.A.

PH.D.

[FIVE DEGREES BELOW ZERO]

What is the meaning of Wowolfol?

[A WOLF IN SHEEP'S CLOTHING]

What is the meaning of:

BRE^Ad

[SHORTENING BREAD]

Name a word of six letters where L is in the middle, is in the beginning, and is in the end.

[ISLAND]

Is it true that Chicago begins with *C*, and
ends with *E?*   [YES, THEY DO]

What is the meaning of:
                    C
                        O
                            N
                                [CONDESCENDING]

Special Rations

That make you:

Warm	CONFLAG RATION
Warmer	INCINE RATION
Cold	REFRIGE RATION
Less	EVAPO RATION
Miserable	FRUST RATION
Well	OPE RATION
Long-lived	MODE RATION
Gifted	INSPI RATION
Last	DU RATION
Full	SATU RATION
Leave	EMIG RATION
Ugly	DISFIGU RATION
Vote	REGIST RATION
Porous	INFILT RATION
Hot	PERSPI RATION
Gay	CELEB RATION

Special Nations

The nation of

Murderers	*is*	ASSASSI NATION
Scholars		EXAMI NATION
Doctors		VACCI NATION
Lunatics		HALLUCI NATION
Light		ILLUMI NATION
Glamorous Gals		FASCI NATION
Fearful Ones		CONSTER NATION
Bigots		DISCRIMI NATION
Poets		IMAGI NATION
Delayers		PROCRASTI NATION
Generous Ones		DO NATION
Regular People		ELIMI NATION
Plotters		MACHI NATION
Prophets		DAM NATION
Chess Players		COMBI NATION
Heavy Sleepers		HIBER NATION